SWING IT, SUNNY

JENNIFER L. HOLM & MATTHEW HOLM
WITH COLOR BY LARK PIEN

graphix
AN IMPRINT OF
■SCHOLASTIC

Library of Congress data available

ISBN 978-0-545-74170-5 (hardcover)
ISBN 978-0-545-74172-9 (paperback)

10 9 8 7 6 5 4 3 2 1   17 18 19 20 21

Printed in China 62
First edition, September 2017
Edited by David Levithan
Lettering by Fawn Lau
Color by Lark Pien
Book design by Phil Falco
Creative Director: David Saylor

For Neelam and Neeta

CHAPTER ONE:
The Sunny Show

Starring Sunny!
(as herself)

♪ She's just a **regular girl** in a regular **world!**

♪ Her **MOM'S** always **busy**

♪ Her **dad's** always **groovy!**

Her little brother's always silly!

There's her best friend, Deb!

And don't forget Gramps!

It's The Sunny Show!

7

9

CHAPTER TWO:
Trophy

I'm going to Deb's.

SCREECH!

SCREEEE

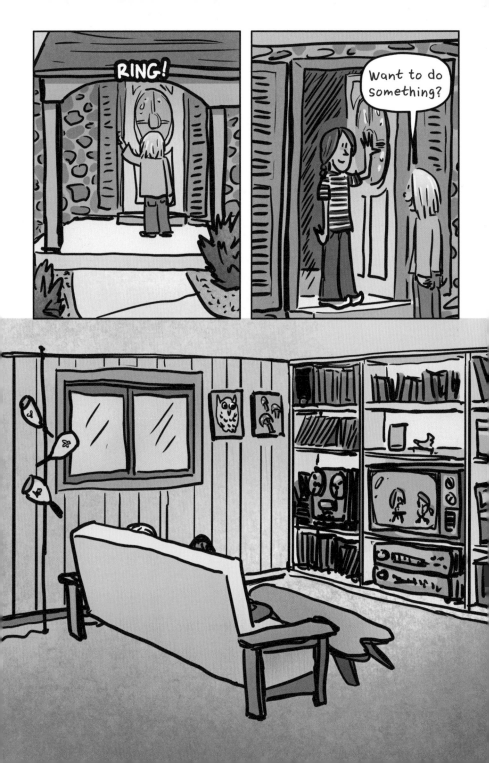

You have any ideas of what we can be for Halloween?

Not yet.

I guess we can always go as babies again.

SHAKE SHAKE

LAST YEAR

32

GENERAL HOSPITAL!

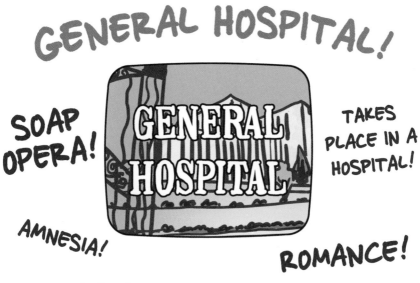

SOAP OPERA!

TAKES PLACE IN A HOSPITAL!

AMNESIA!

ROMANCE!

MISTAKEN IDENTITIES!

FAMILY SECRETS!

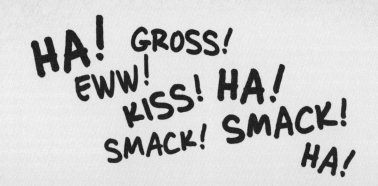

CHAPTER FOUR:
Oh, Brother!

Summy!

POP POP POP POP

Summy!

CRASH!

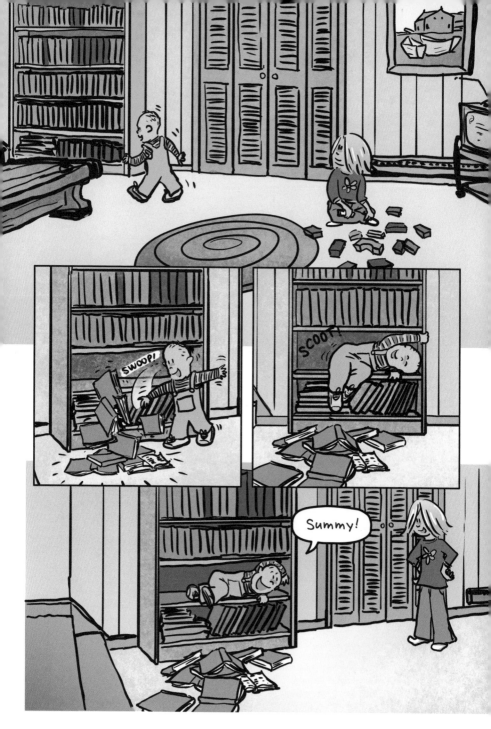

43

49

CHAPTER SIX:
Dress up

65

The Poconos

August 1971

SPLASH

SWISH!

CHAPTER SEVEN:
Trick

HA HA HA!
HA HA HA HA!

That was too easy!

Yeah!

RUSTLE...

Thanksgiving Day.

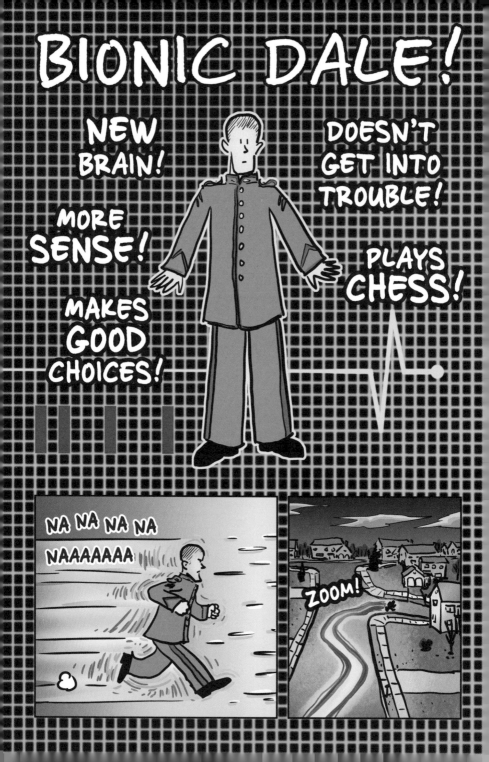

CHAPTER NINE:
Donny & Marie

Well, I've got TV dinners after you've finished your "super-secret stuff!"
Salisbury steak and fried chicken.

TV DINNERS!!!!

CHAPTER TEN:
Pet Rock

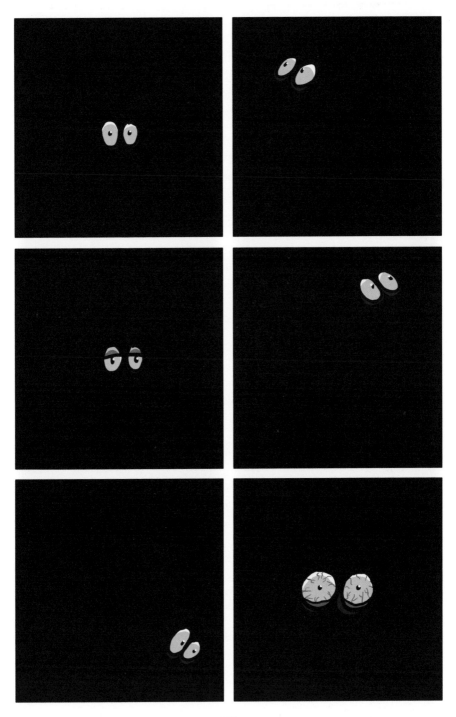

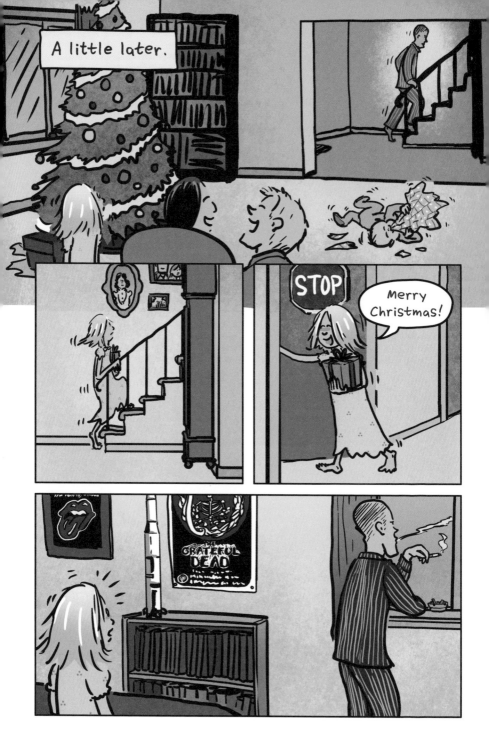

Later.

A few days later.

SLAM

135

CHAPTER THIRTEEN:
Snowbird

A few days later.

CHAPTER FOURTEEN:
Thaw

The next day.

Someone's moving into the DiGennerros' house.

I heard they sold it to someone in town.

I'm going to miss those deer.

Do they have any kids?

I think there's one girl.

I thought I'd take some cookies over a little later.

CHAPTER FIFTEEN:
Sandbox

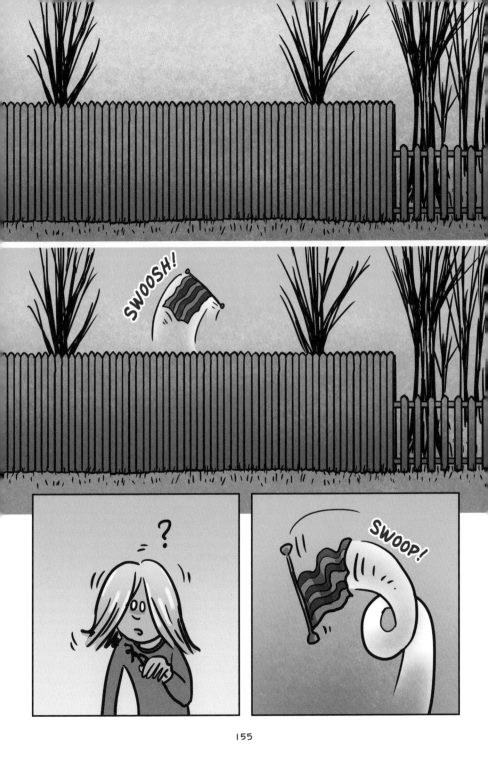

CLICK!

Uh, your flag...

Sorry about that! I was trying a new trick!

Oh, he's so cute!

BOW

CHAPTER SIXTEEN:
Plunger

Later.
Finally! I think I got it.
FLUSH!
Now that that's done, want to see the place?
NOD

Do you think we watch too much TV?

Are you kidding? We have four whole channels and UHF!

There aren't enough hours in the day to watch everything!

SHRUG

True.

GILLIGAN'S ISLAND

CHAPTER NINETEEN:
Wings

Sunny, you're a **GREAT** kid.

I am?

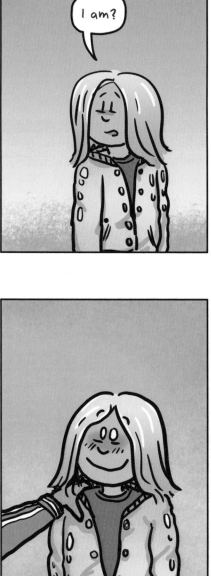

If I had a little sister, I'd want her to be just like YOU.

PUSH

CHAPTER TWENTY: Swing

Later.

It's starting to feel like summer now.

I'm going over to Neela's!

212

A NOTE FROM JENNIFER L. HOLM & MATTHEW HOLM

We were inspired to have Sunny learn how to use a swing flag because Jenni used to do it herself!

ACKNOWLEDGMENTS

We are so grateful to all the wonderful people who help us to continue Sunny's journey. With special thanks to David Levithan, Phil Falco, Lark Pien, Fawn Lau, Cyndi Koon, David Saylor, Lizette Serrano, and Alexandria Terry. As always, many thanks to Jill Grinberg for her incredible support.

JENNIFER L. HOLM & MATTHEW HOLM are the award-winning brother-sister team behind the Babymouse and Squish series, as well as the first Sunny book, SUNNY SIDE UP. Jennifer is also the author of many acclaimed novels, including three Newbery Honor books and the NEW YORK TIMES bestseller THE FOURTEENTH GOLDFISH. Matthew's most recent novel is MARVIN AND THE MOTHS, written with Jonathan Follett.

LARK PIEN, the colorist of SUNNY SIDE UP and SWING IT, SUNNY, is an indie cartoonist from Oakland, California. She has published many comics and is the colorist for Printz Award winner AMERICAN BORN CHINESE, and BOXERS & SAINTS. Her characters Long Tail Kitty and Mr. Elephanter have been adapted into children's books.